FOR CLARINET

PUBLISHED BY

WISE PUBLICATIONS

8/9 FRITH STREET, LONDON W1D 3JB, ENGLAND.

EXCLUSIVE DISTRIBUTORS:

MUSIC SALES LIMITED

DISTRIBUTION CENTRE, NEWMARKET ROAD, BURY ST. EDMUNDS, SUFFOLK IP33 3YB, ENGLAND.

MUSIC SALES PTY LIMITED

120 ROTHSCHILD AVENUE, ROSEBERY, NSW 2018, AUSTRALIA.

ORDER NO. AM979803

ISBN 1-84449-437-3

THIS BOOK © COPYRIGHT 2004 BY WISE PUBLICATIONS.

COMPILED BY NICK CRISPIN

MUSIC ARRANGED BY JACK LONG

MUSIC PROCESSED BY NOTE-ORIOUS PRODUCTIONS LIMITED

COVER PHOTOGRAPHS COURTESY OF LONDON FEATURES INTERNATIONAL

PRINTED IN MALTA

YOUR GUARANTEE OF QUALITY

AS PUBLISHERS, WE STRIVE TO PRODUCE EVERY BOOK TO THE HIGHEST COMMERCIAL STANDARDS.

THE MUSIC HAS BEEN FRESHLY ENGRAVED AND THE BOOK HAS BEEN CAREFULLY

DESIGNED TO MINIMISE AWKWARD PAGE TURNS AND TO MAKE PLAYING FROM IT A REAL PLEASURE.

PARTICULAR CARE HAS BEEN GIVEN TO SPECIFYING ACID-FREE, NEUTRAL-SIZED PAPER MADE

FROM PULPS WHICH HAVE NOT BEEN ELEMENTAL CHLORINE BLEACHED.

THIS PULP IS FROM FARMED SUSTAINABLE FORESTS AND WAS PRODUCED WITH SPECIAL REGARD FOR THE ENVIRONMENT.

THROUGHOUT, THE PRINTING AND BINDING HAVE BEEN PLANNED TO ENSURE A STURDY,

ATTRACTIVE PUBLICATION WHICH SHOULD GIVE YEARS OF ENJOYMENT.

IF YOUR COPY FAILS TO MEET OUR HIGH STANDARDS, PLEASE INFORM US AND WE WILL GLADLY REPLACE IT.

www.musicsales.com

WISE PUBLICATIONS
PART OF THE MUSIC SALES GROUP

LONDON / NEW YORK / PARIS / SYDNEY / COPENHAGEN / BERLIN / MADRID / TOKYO

Anyone Of Us (Stupid Mistake)

Words & Music by Jorgen Elofsson, Per Magnusson & David Kreuger

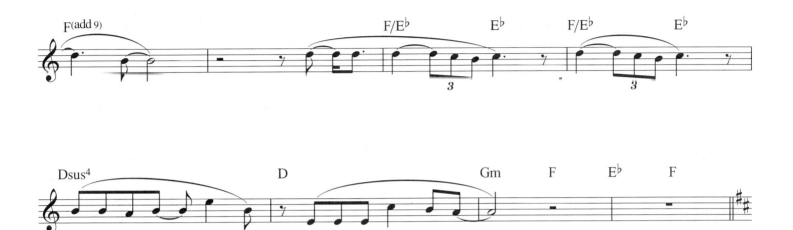

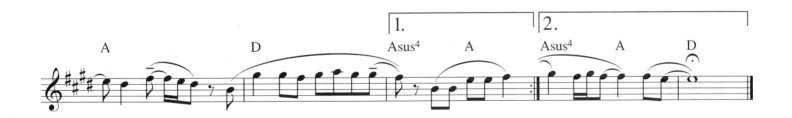

Always On My Mind

Words & Music by Wayne Thompson, Mark James & Johnny Christopher

Beautiful

Words & Music by Linda Perry

Big Sur

Words by Conor Deasy. Music by Conor Deasy, Kevin Horan, Pádraic McMahon, Daniel Ryan & Ben Carrigan
Contains elements from "Theme From The Monkees" – Words & Music by Tommy Boyce & Bobby Hart

Born To Try

Words & Music by Delta Goodrem & Audius Mtawarira

Bridge Over Troubled Water

Words & Music by Paul Simon

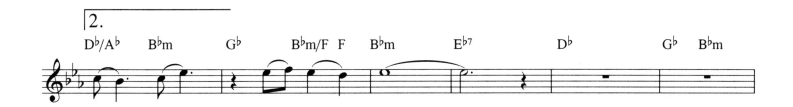

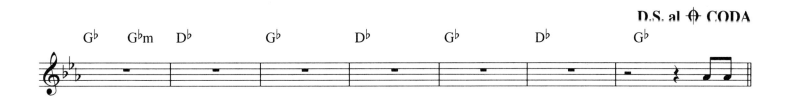

D.S. al ϕ CODA

ϕ CODA

Brown Eyed Girl

Words & Music by Van Morrison

Build Me Up Buttercup

Words & Music by Tony Macaulay & Michael D'Abo

Careless Whisper

Words & Music by George Michael & Andrew Ridgeley

Can't Get You Out Of My Head

Words & Music by Cathy Dennis & Rob Davis

Caught In The Middle

Words & Music by Ben Adams, Paul Marazzi, Chris Porter & Rick Mitra

Clocks

Words & Music by Guy Berryman, Chris Martin, Jon Buckland & Will Champion

Colourblind

Words & Music by Darius, Pete Glenister & Denny Lew

Constant Craving

Words & Music by K.D. Lang & Ben Mink

Cry Me A River

Words & Music by Justin Timberlake, Scott Storch & Tim Mosley

Don't Know Why

Words & Music by Jesse Harris

Don't Speak

Words & Music by Eric Stefani & Gwen Stefani

Don't Stop Movin'

Words & Music by Simon Ellis, Sheppard Solomon & S Club 7

To ⊕ CODA

D.S. al ⊕ CODA

Fine

⊕ CODA

Play three times

D.S.S. al Fine

Eternal Flame

Words & Music by Billy Steinberg, Tom Kelly & Susanna Hoffs

Evergreen

Words & Music by Jorgen Elofsson, Per Magnusson & David Kreuger

Electrical Storm

Words by Bono. Music by U2

Every Little Thing She Does Is Magic

Words & Music by Sting

Feel

Words & Music by Robbie Williams & Guy Chambers

Fields Of Gold

Words & Music by Sting

Frozen

Words & Music by Madonna & Patrick Leonard

Flying Without Wings

Words & Music by Steve Mac & Wayne Hector

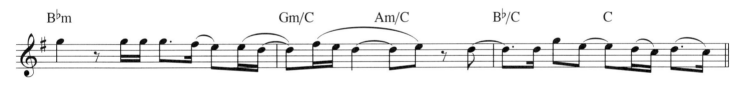

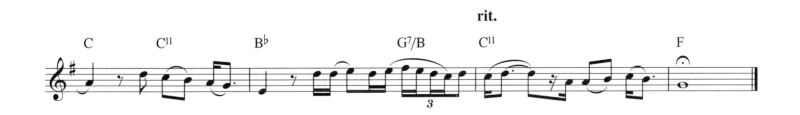

God Only Knows

Words & Music by Brian Wilson & Tony Asher

Gold

Words & Music by Prince

Goldfinger

Words by Leslie Bricusse & Anthony Newley. Music by John Barry

The Great Pretender

Words & Music by Buck Ram

A Hard Day's Night

Words & Music by John Lennon & Paul McCartney

Hello

Words & Music by Lionel Richie

Hero

Words & Music by Enrique Iglesias, Paul Barry & Mark Taylor

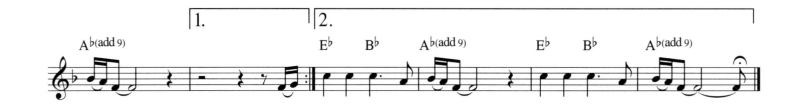

Hopelessly Devoted To You

Words & Music by John Farrar

How Deep Is Your Love

Words & Music by Barry Gibb, Maurice Gibb & Robin Gibb

Human Nature

Words & Music by Steve Porcaro & John Bettis

Hunter

Words & Music by Dido Armstrong & Rollo Armstrong

I Drove All Night

Words & Music by Tom Kelly & Billy Steinberg

I Get The Sweetest Feeling

Words & Music by Van McCoy & Alicia Evelyn

I Got You (I Feel Good)

Words & Music by James Brown

I Heard It Through The Grapevine

Words & Music by Norman Whitfield & Barrett Strong

I Try

Words by Macy Gray

Music by Macy Gray, Jeremy Ruzumna, Jinsoo Lim & David Wilder

I'm Gonna Getcha Good!

Words & Music by Shania Twain & Robert John "Mutt" Lange

I'm With You

Words & Music by Avril Lavigne, Lauren Christy, Scott Spock & Graham Edwards

If I Could Turn Back The Hands Of Time

Words & Music by R. Kelly

If Tomorrow Never Comes

Words & Music by Garth Brooks & Kent Blazy

If You're Not The One

Words & Music by Daniel Bedingfield

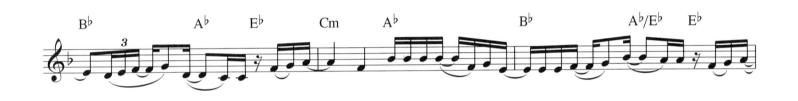

If You Come Back

Words & Music by Ray Ruffin, Nicole Formescu, Ian Hope & Lee Brennan

Imagine

Words & Music by John Lennon

It's My Life

Words & Music by Mark Hollis & Tim Friese-Greene

La Bamba

Music: Traditional

Lambada

Words by Gonzalo Hermosa, Ulises Hermosa, Alberto Maravi, Marcia Ferreira & Jose Ari
Music by Gonzalo Hermosa & Ulises Hermosa

The Life Of Riley

Words & Music by Ian Broudie

Little Lies

Words & Music by Christine McVie & Eddy Quintela

The Long And Winding Road

Words & Music by John Lennon & Paul McCartney

Mad World

Words & Music by Roland Orzabal

Mamma Mia

Words & Music by Benny Andersson, Bjorn Ulvaeus & Stig Anderson

My Heart Will Go On
(Love Theme From 'Titanic')

Words by Will Jennings. Music by James Horner

Natural Blues

Words by Vera Hall
Music by Vera Hall & Moby

No More "I Love You's"

Words & Music by D. Freeman & J. Hughes

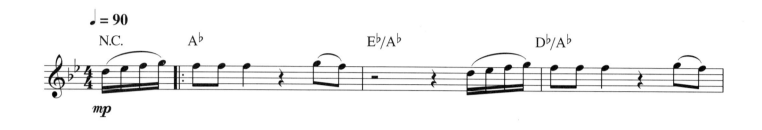

Nothing Compares 2 U

Words & Music by Prince

One Day I'll Fly Away

Words by Will Jennings. Music by Joe Sample

Oops!... I Did It Again

Words & Music by Max Martin & Rami

The Power Of Love

Words & Music by Holly Johnson, Mark O'Toole, Peter Gill & Brian Nash

Pure And Simple

Words & Music by Tim Hawes, Pete Kirtley & Alison Clarkson

Pure Shores

Words & Music by William Orbit & Shaznay Lewis

Rise

Words & Music by Bob Dylan, Gabrielle, Ferdy Unger-Hamilton & Ollie Dagois

Run For Cover

Words & Music by Cameron McVey, Johnny Lipsey,
Paul Simm, Siobhan Donaghy, Keisha Buchanan & Mutya Buena

Road Rage

Words & Music by Cerys Matthews, Mark Roberts, Aled Richards, Paul Jones & Owen Powell

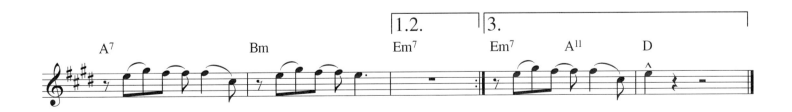

Sail Away

Words & Music by David Gray

Sing

Words & Music by Fran Healy

(Sittin' On) The Dock Of The Bay

Words & Music by Steve Cropper & Otis Redding

(Something Inside) So Strong

Words & Music by Labi Siffre

Somethin' Stupid

Words & Music by C. Carson Parks

Stand By Me

Words & Music by Ben E. King, Jerry Leiber & Mike Stoller

Suspicious Minds

Words & Music by Francis Zambon

Sweet Caroline

Words & Music by Neil Diamond

Tainted Love

Words & Music by Ed Cobb

Take Me To The River

Words & Music by Al Green & Mabon Hodges

Take On Me

Words & Music by Morten Harket, Mags Furuholmen & Pal Waaktaar

Tears In Heaven

Words & Music by Eric Clapton & Will Jennings

There She Goes

Words & Music by Lee Mavers

The Tide Is High

Words & Music by John Holt, Howard Barrett & Tyrone Evans

Time After Time

Words & Music by Cyndi Lauper & Robert Hyman

True Faith

Words & Music by Peter Hook, Stephen Hague,
Bernard Sumner, Gillian Gilbert & Stephen Morris

Video Killed The Radio Star

Words & Music by Geoffrey Downes, Trevor Horn & Bruce Woolley

Vienna

Words & Music by Midge Ure, Billy Currie, Warren Cann & Christopher Allen

Walking Away

Words & Music by Craig David & Mark Hill

Waterloo

Words & Music by Benny Andersson, Bjorn Ulvaeus & Stig Anderson

What A Wonderful World

Words & Music by George Weiss & Bob Thiele

What If

Words & Music by Steve McCutcheon & Wayne Hector

Whenever, Wherever

Words by Shakira & Gloria Estefan. Music by Shakira & Tim Mitchell

Whole Again

Words & Music by Stuart Kershaw, Andy McCluskey, Bill Padley & Jeremy Godfrey

Wonderful Life

Words & Music by Colin Vearncombe

Yellow

Words & Music by Guy Berryman, Jon Buckland, Will Champion & Chris Martin

Yesterday

Words & Music by John Lennon & Paul McCartney

You Are Not Alone

Words & Music by Robert Kelly

You Wear It Well

Words & Music by Rod Stewart & Martin Quittenton

Your Song

Words & Music by Elton John & Bernie Taupin

You're So Vain

Words & Music by Carly Simon

Optional: play octave down

2/07 (61280)